The Soil Energy Solution

Harnessing the Power of Soil-Microbe-Powered Fuel Cell for Sustainable and Greener Energy Generation

Roy J. Vesey

All rights reserved. No part of this publication may be reproduced, distributed, or transmitted in any form or by any means, including photocopying, recording, or other electronic or mechanical methods, without the prior written permission of the publisher, except in the case of brief quotations embodied in critical reviews and certain other noncommercial uses permitted by copyright law.

© Roy J. Vesey, 2024

TABLE OF CONTENT

Introduction..4
Overview of Soil-Microbe-Powered Fuel Cells..6
Importance of Sustainable Energy Solutions.. 8
Objectives of the Research....................10

Background....................................14
Evolution of Microbial Fuel Cells (MFCs). 14
Challenges with Traditional MFCs..........17
Need for Sustainable Alternatives to Batteries..20

Research Methodology....................23
Design and Development of the Soil-Microbe-Powered Fuel Cell............23
Testing Procedures and Parameters..... 26
Comparison with Existing Technologies... 29

Results and Findings......................32
Performance of the Soil-Microbe-Powered Fuel Cell............32
Power Output and Efficiency..................34
Adaptability to Various Soil Conditions 36

Applications and Implications........ 39
Utilization of Soil-Powered Technology in Precision Agriculture............................ 39
Potential for Green Infrastructure and Environmental Monitoring................... 42
Contributions to Sustainable Energy Solutions.. 44

Technology Overview...................... 48
Components and Operation of the Soil-Microbe-Powered Fuel Cell........... 48
Advantages Of Traditional Battery Systems... 53
Wireless Communication and Data Transmission..57

Design and Engineering.................. 63
Engineering Challenges and Solutions. 63
Unique Features of the Perpendicular Design... 67
Incorporation of 3D-Printed Components 70

Accessibility and Open Source Initiatives... 76
Public Access to Designs, Tutorials, and Simulation Tools....................................76
Encouraging Collaboration and Further

3

Development..................................... 80
Advantages of Open Source Approach in
Science and Engineering....................... 82
**Future Directions and Research
Opportunities............................... 86**
Potential Improvements and
Enhancements...................................... 86
Exploration of Fully Biodegradable
Materials.. 89
Integration with Emerging Technologies
and IoT... 91
Environmental and Social Impact... 97
Reduction of Electronic Waste and Toxic
Chemicals... 97
Contribution to Sustainable Development
Goals... 100
Implications for Global Energy and
Environmental Policy.......................... 103
Conclusion.....................................107
Summary of Key Findings and
Contributions....................................... 107
Significance of Soil-Microbe-Powered
Fuel Cells in Sustainable Energy
Landscape... 109
Call to Action for Further Research and

Implementation 111

Introduction

In recent scientific breakthroughs, researchers at Northwestern University have pioneered a revolutionary approach to sustainable energy by developing soil-microbe-powered fuel cells. This innovative technology harnesses the power of microbes residing in the soil to generate electricity, presenting a promising alternative to conventional energy sources. The following sections delve into the overview of soil-microbe-powered fuel cells, emphasize the critical importance of sustainable energy solutions, and outline the specific objectives of the groundbreaking research.

Overview of Soil-Microbe-Powered Fuel Cells

Soil-microbe-powered fuel cells represent a novel concept in the realm of renewable energy. These fuel cells, about the size of a standard paperback book, leverage the inherent electrical capabilities of microbes present in the soil. Unlike traditional fuel cells that rely on chemical reactions to generate electricity, soil-microbe-powered fuel cells tap into the microbial activity in the soil, converting it into a sustainable source of power.

The basic principle behind these fuel cells involves the use of soil-based microbial fuel cells (MFCs), which have been known since 1911. In a typical MFC, there are an anode, cathode, and electrolyte. However, instead of using chemicals, these fuel cells utilize bacteria naturally donating electrons to nearby conductors. This flow of electrons creates an electric circuit, effectively generating electricity. The innovation lies in the adaptation of MFCs to operate reliably in low-moisture conditions, making them suitable for a variety of applications.

Northwestern University researchers have taken this concept a step further by developing a unique prototype with a perpendicular design of the anode and cathode. This design, coupled with 3D-printed components, allows the fuel cell to function effectively in both wet and dry conditions. The groundbreaking technology opens the door to a wide range of applications, particularly in precision agriculture and environmental monitoring.

Importance of Sustainable Energy Solutions

The quest for sustainable energy solutions has never been more critical than in the current era of rapid technological advancement and increasing energy demands. Conventional energy sources, often reliant on finite fossil fuels, contribute significantly to environmental degradation, climate change, and geopolitical conflicts. The importance of transitioning to sustainable alternatives is underscored by the need to mitigate these pressing global challenges.

Soil-microbe-powered fuel cells offer a compelling solution to the environmental impact of traditional energy sources. By tapping into the abundance of microbes in the soil, this technology provides a renewable and eco-friendly energy option.

Unlike batteries that contain toxic and flammable chemicals, soil-microbe-powered fuel cells operate with minimal environmental impact. Furthermore, the research at Northwestern University focuses on making the designs and technology accessible to the public, fostering a culture of open-source collaboration for widespread implementation.

The significance of sustainable energy solutions extends beyond environmental considerations. It addresses issues of energy security, reducing dependence on fossil fuels, and mitigating the geopolitical tensions associated with their extraction. Additionally, as the world embraces digitalization with an increasing number of electronic devices, finding sustainable energy sources becomes imperative to prevent further strain on resources and the generation of electronic waste.

Objectives of the Research

The research conducted by the Northwestern University-led team is driven by a set of clear and ambitious objectives aimed at advancing the field of renewable energy and addressing the challenges associated with traditional power sources. The primary objectives can be summarized as follows:

1. **Develop a Reliable Soil-Microbe-Powered Fuel Cell:** The core objective is to design and develop a soil-microbe-powered fuel cell that is not only reliable but also performs effectively in various environmental conditions, including both wet and dry soil. This involves innovative engineering to overcome historical challenges associated with

the performance of microbial fuel cells.

2. **Demonstrate Practical Applications:** The researchers seek to demonstrate the practical applications of the soil-microbe-powered fuel cell by powering sensors relevant to precision agriculture and environmental monitoring. This involves testing the technology in real-world scenarios to showcase its viability for powering low-energy devices used in these fields.

3. **Ensure Accessibility and Open Source Collaboration:** A key objective is to make the technology accessible to the public by releasing all designs, tutorials, and simulation tools. By adopting an open-source approach, the research team aims to encourage collaboration, allowing

others to build upon the technology and contribute to its further development.

4. **Contribute to Sustainable Energy Solutions:** The overarching goal of the research is to contribute to sustainable energy solutions by providing an alternative to traditional batteries and promoting environmentally friendly practices. The focus on harnessing energy from soil microbes aligns with the broader objective of reducing the environmental impact of power generation.

In pursuit of these objectives, the Northwestern University-led team has embarked on a multidisciplinary journey, combining engineering, environmental science, and open-source principles to usher in a new era of sustainable energy solutions. The research not only addresses immediate challenges in precision agriculture but also lays the groundwork for scalable and eco-friendly energy alternatives in the ever-expanding landscape of digital technology.

Background

Renewable energy research has seen remarkable advancements in recent years, and one noteworthy innovation is the development of soil-microbe-powered fuel cells. To comprehend the significance of this breakthrough, it is essential to delve into the background, exploring the evolution of microbial fuel cells (MFCs), understanding the challenges associated with traditional MFCs, and recognizing the urgent need for sustainable alternatives to conventional batteries.

Evolution of Microbial Fuel Cells (MFCs)

The roots of microbial fuel cells can be traced back over a century to 1911 when the concept first made its appearance. Microbial fuel cells operate as energy converters, functioning like batteries but with a unique mechanism. Instead of relying on chemical reactions, MFCs leverage the electrogenic capabilities of bacteria to generate electricity.

In a standard microbial fuel cell, there are key components: an anode, a cathode, and an electrolyte. Unlike traditional batteries, MFCs don't utilize chemicals to create electrical energy. Instead, they harness bacteria present in the environment, typically in soil or water. These bacteria, undergoing metabolic processes, naturally donate electrons to nearby conductors, initiating an electric circuit. The flow of electrons from the anode to the cathode creates a current, producing electrical energy.

Despite their early conception, the widespread practical use of microbial fuel cells has faced challenges over the years. The original idea of tapping into the microbial world for energy generation was revolutionary but presented several limitations, particularly in terms of reliability, output power, and adaptability to varying environmental conditions.

Challenges with Traditional MFCs

While the concept of microbial fuel cells has been intriguing, practical implementation faced hurdles that hindered their widespread adoption. One of the primary challenges stems from the inherent variability in microbial activity. Microbes thrive in diverse environments, and the performance of microbial fuel cells is highly dependent on the specific microbial communities present.

Traditional MFCs, designed with parallel positioning of the anode and cathode, struggled to operate consistently in low-moisture conditions. To produce electricity, microbial fuel cells require a certain level of hydration and oxygenation, making them less effective when buried in dry soil. This unreliability has stymied efforts to make practical use of microbial fuel cells, especially in scenarios where consistent moisture levels cannot be guaranteed.

The low output power of traditional microbial fuel cells has been another significant challenge. The amount of energy generated was often insufficient for practical applications, limiting their usability. Additionally, the lack of a standardized design that could adapt to various environmental conditions hindered the scalability and versatility of microbial fuel cells.

In essence, the challenges with traditional MFCs revolved around their unreliable performance, low output power, and limited adaptability to diverse conditions. These limitations prompted researchers to explore innovative approaches to enhance the effectiveness of microbial fuel cells and unlock their potential for practical applications.

Need for Sustainable Alternatives to Batteries

The global reliance on traditional batteries, often powered by finite and environmentally detrimental resources, has prompted a growing recognition of the need for sustainable alternatives. Conventional batteries, frequently containing toxic and flammable chemicals, pose environmental risks, especially when improperly disposed of, leading to soil and water contamination.

As societies continue to advance technologically, the proliferation of electronic devices has become a ubiquitous part of modern life. However, the environmental consequences of manufacturing, using, and disposing of traditional batteries are alarming. The extraction of minerals for battery production contributes to ecological damage, and the disposal of used batteries contributes to the growing crisis of electronic waste.

Sustainable alternatives to batteries are crucial not only to mitigate environmental impact but also to ensure a continuous and reliable power source for the increasing number of electronic devices. The demand for energy is escalating, and finding eco-friendly solutions becomes imperative to address both current and future energy needs sustainably.

In this context, soil-microbe-powered fuel cells emerge as a promising alternative. By utilizing the abundant and natural microbial activity in the soil, these fuel cells offer a renewable and environmentally friendly energy source. The research at Northwestern University specifically addresses the need for sustainable alternatives to batteries by exploring the potential of soil-microbe-powered technology in powering low-energy devices without the environmental drawbacks associated with traditional batteries.

The background of microbial fuel cells, the challenges faced by traditional MFCs, and the pressing need for sustainable alternatives to batteries collectively set the stage for the pioneering research conducted by Northwestern University. The evolution of this technology holds the promise of transforming how we approach energy generation, emphasizing sustainability, reliability, and environmental responsibility.

Research Methodology

Design and Development of the Soil-Microbe-Powered Fuel Cell

The research conducted by the Northwestern University-led team on soil-microbe-powered fuel cells involves a meticulous and innovative methodology that encompasses the design and development of the technology. The goal is to create a reliable and efficient fuel cell capable of harnessing energy from soil microbes and powering low-energy devices. The design and development phase is a crucial aspect of the research methodology, setting the foundation for the subsequent testing and comparison phases.

The design process begins with a thorough understanding of microbial fuel cells (MFCs) and their historical challenges. Drawing inspiration from the traditional MFC structure, the Northwestern team introduces a unique perpendicular design of the anode and cathode. Unlike the conventional parallel design, this innovative approach aims to overcome issues related to low-moisture conditions and maximize the fuel cell's adaptability to various environmental settings.

The anode, typically made of carbon felt, is positioned horizontally to the ground's surface, buried in the soil. The cathode, made of an inert, conductive metal, is placed vertically atop the anode. This vertical orientation ensures that the top end of the fuel cell is flush with the ground's surface. A 3D-printed cap, designed to keep debris out while allowing consistent airflow, rests on top of the device. The lower end of the cathode remains submerged in the soil, ensuring hydration from the moist surroundings.

The use of 3D-printed components showcases the interdisciplinary nature of the research, combining principles of engineering, environmental science, and material science. The design not only addresses challenges related to moisture levels but also considers potential flooding scenarios by incorporating waterproofing materials and allowing gradual drying of the cathode after a flood.

This thoughtful design is intended to optimize the microbial fuel cell for real-world applications, particularly in precision agriculture and environmental monitoring. By making the fuel cell compatible with diverse soil conditions and weather fluctuations, the design phase sets the stage for a practical and robust solution to harness energy from soil microbes.

Testing Procedures and Parameters

With the designed soil-microbe-powered fuel cell in hand, the research methodology transitions into the testing phase. Rigorous testing procedures and parameters are employed to evaluate the performance, efficiency, and adaptability of the fuel cell in real-world conditions. The objective is to validate the design's effectiveness and assess its practical applications, especially in powering sensors relevant to precision agriculture and environmental monitoring.

The researchers begin by deploying the fuel cell in various soil environments, ranging from dry conditions to water-logged scenarios. This diverse testing landscape is crucial for assessing the adaptability of the fuel cell and its ability to function in different moisture levels. Continuous monitoring allows the team to collect data on power output, stability, and overall performance.

One of the key parameters tested is the fuel cell's ability to generate power consistently in both wet and dry conditions. This is a significant advancement compared to traditional microbial fuel cells, which often struggle in low-moisture settings. The researchers aim to demonstrate that the perpendicular design, coupled with other innovative features, allows the fuel cell to overcome historical challenges and operate reliably under varying environmental conditions.

To simulate practical applications, the fuel cell is used to power sensors measuring soil moisture and detecting touch. These sensors mimic the requirements of precision agriculture, where continuous monitoring of environmental variables is crucial for optimizing crop yields. The testing phase evaluates the fuel cell's capacity to provide a sustainable and long-lasting power source for such low-energy devices.

Wireless communication is another aspect tested during this phase. The researchers equipped the soil-powered sensor with a tiny antenna to transmit data to a neighboring base station by reflecting existing radio frequency signals. This wireless communication feature enhances the fuel cell's practicality in real-world applications, allowing data to be transmitted seamlessly from remote locations.

Comparison with Existing Technologies

As the soil-microbe-powered fuel cell undergoes rigorous testing, the research methodology includes a crucial component: the comparison with existing technologies. This comparative analysis aims to highlight the strengths and advantages of the novel fuel cell for conventional batteries, solar panels, and other renewable energy solutions. By positioning the soil-microbe-powered technology within the broader context of existing alternatives, the researchers can showcase its potential impact and unique contributions.

Traditional batteries, often containing toxic and flammable chemicals, present environmental risks, and their finite lifespan contributes to electronic waste concerns. Solar panels, while harnessing energy from the sun, face limitations in dirty environments, space requirements, and dependence on sunlight. The Northwestern University team addresses these challenges by proposing a soil-microbe-powered fuel cell that operates effectively in various soil conditions, avoids toxic materials, and provides a continuous source of renewable energy.

The comparison also considers the efficiency and longevity of the soil-microbe-powered fuel cell. One of the notable findings of the research is that the fuel cell's power output surpassed similar technologies by 120%. This remarkable efficiency positions it as a competitive and viable alternative for powering low-energy devices in comparison to existing solutions.

Moreover, the researchers emphasize the scalability and accessibility of their technology. All designs, tutorials, and simulation tools are released to the public, fostering an open-source approach that encourages collaboration and further development. This contrasts with the often proprietary and centralized nature of existing technologies, showcasing the potential for a decentralized network of devices powered by soil-microbe fuel cells.

In summary, the research methodology encompasses the design and development of an innovative soil-microbe-powered fuel cell, thorough testing to validate its performance and adaptability, and comparative analysis to position it within the landscape of existing technologies. The results of this comprehensive methodology hold the promise of transforming how we approach sustainable energy solutions, particularly in the context of precision agriculture and environmental monitoring.

Results and Findings

Performance of the Soil-Microbe-Powered Fuel Cell

The soil-microbe-powered fuel cell developed by the Northwestern University-led research team demonstrated remarkable performance in harnessing energy from microbial activity in the soil. Through rigorous testing and experimentation, the researchers observed consistent and reliable power generation, positioning the technology as a promising alternative to conventional energy sources.

The fuel cell's performance was evaluated under both laboratory and real-world conditions, showcasing its ability to operate effectively in diverse environments. The researchers buried the fuel cell in soil, simulating real-world applications, and monitored its performance over an extended period. The results revealed a stable and continuous energy output, highlighting the potential for long-term, sustainable energy solutions.

One key aspect of the fuel cell's performance was its resilience to changes in soil moisture levels. Unlike traditional microbial fuel cells that often struggle in low-moisture conditions, the soil-microbe-powered fuel cell exhibited consistent power generation across a range of soil moisture levels. This adaptability is crucial for practical applications, especially in agricultural settings where soil conditions can vary significantly.

Moreover, the researchers explored the fuel cell's response to different organic carbon levels in the soil. The fuel cell effectively utilizes organic carbon as a fuel source for microbial activity, emphasizing its ability to generate energy as long as there is a supply of organic carbon. This finding suggests that the fuel cell has the potential for sustained operation in a variety of soil types and compositions.

Power Output and Efficiency

The power output and efficiency of the soil-microbe-powered fuel cell surpassed expectations, marking a significant advancement in microbial fuel cell technology. The researchers carefully measured the electrical output of the fuel cell across various conditions and compared it to existing technologies. The results indicated a notable increase in power output, making the fuel cell a competitive and viable option for powering low-energy devices.

On average, the soil-microbe-powered fuel cell generated 68 times more power than required to operate the sensors it was designed for. This surplus energy opens up possibilities for additional applications or the integration of more demanding devices, showcasing the potential scalability of the technology.

Furthermore, the fuel cell's efficiency was evaluated by considering its energy output concerning the organic carbon content in the soil. The efficiency remained consistently high, demonstrating the effectiveness of the fuel cell in converting microbial activity into electrical energy. This efficiency is crucial for the practical implementation of the technology, ensuring that it can meet the energy demands of real-world applications.

The researchers also compared the soil-microbe-powered fuel cell with other existing microbial fuel cell technologies. The results indicated a remarkable 120% improvement in power output, emphasizing the innovation and superiority of the perpendicular design adopted in this fuel cell. This increased efficiency positions the technology as a frontrunner in the quest for sustainable and efficient energy solutions.

Adaptability to Various Soil Conditions

A key breakthrough in the research was the fuel cell's exceptional adaptability to various soil conditions. Traditional microbial fuel cells often face challenges in maintaining optimal performance in dry or waterlogged soils. In contrast, the soil-microbe-powered fuel cell demonstrated a robust performance across a spectrum of soil moisture levels, showcasing its versatility and reliability.

The unique design, featuring a perpendicular arrangement of the anode and cathode, played a pivotal role in ensuring adaptability. This design allowed the fuel cell to remain effective even in dry conditions by facilitating consistent airflow and preventing the accumulation of debris. The 3D-printed cap, strategically placed above the ground, shielded the device from external elements while enabling essential air exchange.

The adaptability of the fuel cell was further highlighted in its response to fluctuations in soil moisture. The vertical design ensured that the lower end of the cathode remained hydrated, even when the surface soil dried out. This innovative approach addressed a longstanding challenge in microbial fuel cell technology, where maintaining hydration in low-moisture conditions had proven difficult.

Additionally, the researchers coated part of the cathode with waterproofing material, allowing the fuel cell to withstand potential floods. The gradual drying capability of the vertical design post-flood ensured the continued functionality of the fuel cell. This adaptability to environmental changes positions the soil-microbe-powered fuel cell as a reliable and resilient solution for various real-world applications.

In conclusion, the results and findings of the Northwestern University-led research underscore the soil-microbe-powered fuel cell's exceptional performance, high power output, efficiency, and adaptability to diverse soil conditions. These achievements mark a significant milestone in the development of sustainable energy solutions, opening doors to practical applications in precision agriculture, environmental monitoring, and beyond.

Applications and Implications

Utilization of Soil-Powered Technology in Precision Agriculture

The soil-microbe-powered fuel cell presents a revolutionary advancement with far-reaching applications, particularly in the realm of precision agriculture. This innovative technology has the potential to transform the way farmers gather crucial data about their crops, soil conditions, and overall agricultural environments.

Precision agriculture relies on real-time, accurate information to make informed decisions regarding crop health, nutrient levels, and irrigation requirements. The soil-powered technology offers a sustainable and reliable power source for sensors embedded in the soil. These sensors can continuously monitor various parameters, such as soil moisture, nutrient content, and temperature, providing farmers with actionable insights.

By eliminating the need for traditional batteries or dependence on external power sources, the soil-microbe-powered fuel cell addresses a significant challenge in deploying sensors across large agricultural landscapes. Farmers can now seamlessly integrate these sensors into their fields, enabling comprehensive data collection without the hassle of frequent maintenance or battery replacements. This not only streamlines the monitoring process but also enhances the efficiency of precision agriculture practices.

Furthermore, the adaptability of the fuel cell to different soil conditions ensures its applicability in various agricultural settings. Whether in arid regions or areas prone to heavy rainfall, the technology can consistently power sensors, contributing to a more resilient and sustainable agricultural ecosystem.

The utilization of soil-powered technology in precision agriculture extends beyond basic monitoring. The continuous power supply enables the deployment of advanced sensors capable of detecting specific plant diseases, pest infestations, or even assessing the overall well-being of crops. This level of granularity in data collection empowers farmers to implement targeted interventions, reducing the need for broad-spectrum treatments and minimizing environmental impact.

Potential for Green Infrastructure and Environmental Monitoring

Beyond the agricultural sector, the soil-microbe-powered fuel cell holds significant promise for the development of green infrastructure and environmental monitoring systems. Green infrastructure, characterized by sustainable and nature-based solutions, can benefit from the continuous and eco-friendly power provided by this innovative technology.

Urban green spaces, parks, and environmental restoration projects often incorporate sensors to monitor air quality, soil health, and biodiversity. Traditional power sources for these sensors, such as batteries or solar panels, come with limitations. Batteries require frequent replacement, and solar panels may be inefficient in shaded or densely populated urban areas.

The soil-powered technology offers a decentralized and self-sustaining alternative. Sensors embedded in the ground can draw energy from soil microbes, ensuring continuous operation without the need for external power sources. This not only reduces maintenance efforts but also enhances the reliability of environmental monitoring systems.

In urban environments, where green infrastructure is crucial for mitigating the heat island effect and enhancing overall livability, the soil-microbe-powered fuel cell can play a pivotal role. Sensors powered by this technology can monitor soil moisture levels, detect pollution, and contribute to the overall health of green spaces. This data can inform city planners and policymakers, enabling them to make informed decisions for sustainable urban development.

Furthermore, the fuel cell's adaptability to various soil conditions makes it suitable for deployment in diverse environmental settings. From urban parks to remote natural reserves, the technology offers a scalable solution for creating resilient and effective green infrastructure.

Contributions to Sustainable Energy Solutions

The soil-microbe-powered fuel cell emerges as a key player in the broader landscape of sustainable energy solutions. As the world grapples with the challenges of climate change and seeks alternatives to traditional energy sources, this innovative technology offers a decentralized and environmentally friendly approach to power generation.

One of the primary contributions of soil-powered technology lies in its potential to reduce reliance on conventional batteries, which often contain toxic materials and contribute to electronic waste. By harnessing energy from soil microbes, the fuel cell provides a clean and renewable energy source that aligns with the principles of a circular economy.

The scalability of the technology allows for its integration into various energy-harvesting systems. In addition to powering sensors, the soil-microbe-powered fuel cell could contribute to the energy needs of low-power devices in off-grid or remote locations. This has implications for communities without reliable access to traditional power sources, offering a sustainable alternative for powering essential devices.

Moreover, the open-source approach taken by the researchers in releasing designs and tutorials to the public promotes collaboration and innovation in the development of sustainable energy solutions. This democratization of knowledge can lead to the widespread adoption and adaptation of the technology, fostering a global community focused on addressing energy challenges through environmentally conscious means.

In the context of the Internet of Things (IoT), where the number of connected devices continues to grow, the soil-microbe-powered fuel cell presents a viable solution for powering a decentralized network. Its ability to generate energy as long as there is organic carbon in the soil positions it as a long-lasting and reliable power source for the trillions of devices that may populate the IoT in the future.

In conclusion, the applications and implications of the soil-microbe-powered fuel cell extend from precision agriculture and green infrastructure to contributing to broader sustainable energy solutions. This technology holds the potential to reshape how we approach energy generation, emphasizing eco-friendly, decentralized, and resilient solutions for a more sustainable future.

Technology Overview

Components and Operation of the Soil-Microbe-Powered Fuel Cell

The soil-microbe-powered fuel cell represents a groundbreaking leap in sustainable energy technology. Comprising carefully engineered components, this innovative device taps into the power of microbial activity in the soil to generate electricity. Understanding the key components and the operation of this fuel cell provides insight into its transformative potential.

1. **Anode:-** The anode serves as the point of entry for microbial activity. In the soil, naturally occurring bacteria donate electrons during their metabolic processes. The anode collects these electrons, initiating the flow of electric current.

2. **Cathode:** Positioned perpendicular to the anode, the cathode acts as the exit point for electrons in the electric circuit. As electrons travel from the anode to the cathode, electricity is generated. The cathode's vertical orientation ensures efficient electron flow and contributes to the fuel cell's overall effectiveness.

3. **Electrolyte:** The electrolyte facilitates the movement of ions between the anode and cathode, enabling the completion of the electric circuit. In traditional batteries, chemical reactions within the electrolyte generate electricity. In the soil-microbe-powered fuel cell, the electrolyte supports microbial processes that lead to electron transfer.

4. **Microbial Activity:** Soil microbes, including bacteria, play a crucial role

in this technology. As these microbes break down organic carbon in the soil, they release electrons. The anode captures these electrons, initiating the flow that generates an electric current. The continuous presence of organic carbon ensures a sustainable source of energy for microbial activity.

5. **3D-Printed Cap:** A 3D-printed cap covers the fuel cell, preventing debris from entering while allowing essential air exchange. This cap protects the internal components from external elements, ensuring the longevity and reliability of the fuel cell in real-world applications.

6. **Adaptability Features:** The fuel cell's design incorporates features to enhance adaptability. The vertical arrangement of the cathode, combined with a waterproof coating, enables the fuel cell to remain functional in

varying soil moisture conditions. This adaptability addresses a historical challenge in microbial fuel cell technology.

7. **Air Chamber:** An empty air chamber runs alongside the cathode, promoting consistent airflow. This feature ensures that the microbial processes within the fuel cell receive sufficient oxygen, contributing to sustained and efficient energy generation.

Advantages Of Traditional Battery Systems

The soil-microbe-powered fuel cell presents a paradigm shift in energy storage and generation, offering several advantages over traditional battery systems. These advantages stem from the unique characteristics and operational principles of the fuel cell, making it a promising and sustainable alternative.

1. **Environmental Sustainability:** Unlike traditional batteries that often contain toxic materials harmful to the environment, the soil-microbe-powered fuel cell relies on natural processes and materials. By harnessing energy from soil microbes, it provides a clean and eco-friendly solution, contributing to a reduction in electronic waste.

2. **Renewable and Decentralized:** The fuel cell's reliance on microbial activity fueled by organic carbon in the soil makes it a renewable energy source. As long as there is organic carbon present, the fuel cell can generate electricity, offering a decentralized and sustainable alternative to conventional power sources.

3. **Longevity and Low Maintenance:** Traditional batteries require frequent

replacements and can experience performance degradation over time. In contrast, the soil-microbe-powered fuel cell exhibited longevity during testing, lasting 120% longer than comparable technologies. Its low-maintenance nature makes it an attractive option for applications in remote or hard-to-reach locations.

4. **Adaptability to Soil Conditions:** The fuel cell's innovative design, including the perpendicular arrangement of the anode and cathode, ensures adaptability to various soil conditions. It can operate effectively in both wet and dry environments, overcoming a significant limitation of traditional microbial fuel cells that struggle in low-moisture conditions.

5. **Small Environmental Footprint:** The components of the

soil-microbe-powered fuel cell can be sourced locally, reducing the need for complex supply chains and minimizing the environmental impact associated with the production of batteries. This small environmental footprint aligns with the principles of sustainability and local resource utilization.

6. **Continuous Power Generation:** The fuel cell's ability to generate continuous power, even in low-moisture conditions, sets it apart from conventional batteries and solar panels. This characteristic makes it suitable for applications where uninterrupted power is essential, such as precision agriculture and environmental monitoring.

Wireless Communication and Data Transmission

In addition to its sustainable power generation capabilities, the soil-microbe-powered fuel cell incorporates features for wireless communication and data transmission. This aspect extends the utility of the technology beyond energy generation, enabling seamless connectivity and real-time data transfer in various applications.

1. **Integration of Wireless Technology:** The fuel cell is equipped with a tiny antenna that facilitates wireless communication. This integration enables the transmission of data from sensors powered by the fuel cell to external base stations without the need for

physical connections or additional power sources.

2. **Reflection of Radio Frequency Signals:** The tiny antenna operates by reflecting existing radio frequency signals. This innovative approach eliminates the need for dedicated power-hungry communication systems, leveraging ambient signals to transmit data. This reflects a resource-efficient and sustainable approach to wireless communication.

3. **Practical Applications in Precision Agriculture:** In precision agriculture, where the continuous monitoring of soil conditions is essential, the wireless communication feature enhances the functionality of the soil-microbe-powered fuel cell. Data collected by sensors, powered by the fuel cell, can be transmitted wirelessly to central databases or farm management systems in real time.

4. **Reduction of Maintenance Efforts:** The wireless communication capability reduces the need for physical checks or manual data retrieval from sensors. This not only streamlines data collection processes but also minimizes maintenance efforts, particularly in expansive agricultural fields or remote environmental monitoring locations.

5. **Potential for IoT Integration:** As the number of devices in the Internet of Things (IoT) continues to grow, the soil-microbe-powered fuel cell's wireless communication feature positions it as a potential contributor to a decentralized network of connected devices. Its ability to transmit data wirelessly makes it compatible with the requirements of an interconnected and digitally driven future.

6. **Environmental Monitoring and Green Infrastructure:** In green infrastructure and environmental monitoring applications, the wireless communication feature facilitates the seamless integration of sensor networks. Whether monitoring air quality, soil health, or biodiversity, the fuel cell's wireless connectivity ensures timely and efficient data

transmission for informed decision-making.

In conclusion, the soil-microbe-powered fuel cell not only revolutionizes energy generation but also embraces wireless communication capabilities, making it a versatile solution for precision agriculture, environmental monitoring, and the evolving landscape of interconnected devices. Its sustainable operation, adaptability, and wireless connectivity mark a significant stride toward a more efficient and eco-friendly technological future.

Design and Engineering

Engineering Challenges and Solutions

The development of the soil-microbe-powered fuel cell was not without its share of engineering challenges, yet the research team at Northwestern University demonstrated ingenuity in overcoming these obstacles. Addressing these challenges was crucial for creating a practical and efficient fuel cell that could operate effectively in real-world conditions.

1. **Low-Moisture Operation:** One significant challenge faced by microbial fuel cells is their unreliable performance in low-moisture conditions. Traditional designs

struggle to maintain optimal microbial activity when soil moisture levels decrease. To tackle this, the research team implemented a unique design that enhances hydration and oxygenation, ensuring sustained microbial activity even in dry soil.

2. **Adaptability to Environmental Changes:** Environmental fluctuations, such as floods or changes in soil moisture, posed another challenge. The fuel cell needed to withstand such variations without compromising its performance. The team addressed this by incorporating adaptive features, including a waterproof coating on the cathode and a design that allowed gradual drying after potential floods, ensuring the fuel cell's resilience.

3. **Consistent Airflow:** Microbial processes rely on consistent airflow for

optimal performance. Traditional designs struggled to provide this in buried fuel cells. The engineering team solved this challenge by introducing an empty air chamber alongside the cathode. This design allowed for consistent airflow, promoting the necessary oxygen supply for microbial activity within the fuel cell.

4. **Longevity and Durability:** Ensuring the longevity and durability of the fuel cell presented a vital engineering challenge. Traditional microbial fuel cells often face issues of performance degradation over time. The team addressed this by optimizing the fuel cell's design and materials, resulting in a prototype that demonstrated remarkable longevity, lasting 120% longer than comparable technologies.

5. **Material Selection:** Selecting materials for the fuel cell components was a critical engineering decision. The team opted for cost-effective and readily available materials to ensure accessibility and reduce the environmental impact of production. This decision aligns with the intention to create a sustainable technology with a small environmental footprint.

6. **Integration with Wireless Communication:** Incorporating wireless communication features presented engineering challenges related to power consumption and data transmission. The team overcame this by designing a fuel cell with a tiny antenna capable of reflecting existing radio frequency signals. This innovative solution enabled wireless data transmission without requiring additional power, making the fuel cell suitable for diverse applications.

Unique Features of the Perpendicular Design

The standout feature of the soil-microbe-powered fuel cell lies in its unique perpendicular design, deviating from traditional microbial fuel cell configurations. This unconventional approach brings several advantages that contribute to the fuel cell's superior performance and adaptability.

1. **Enhanced Electron Flow:** The perpendicular design optimizes electron flow within the fuel cell. In traditional designs with parallel anodes and cathodes, electron flow can be less efficient. The perpendicular arrangement ensures a more direct and efficient path for electrons from the anode to the

cathode, maximizing the electricity generated by microbial processes.

2. **Adaptability to Low-Moisture Conditions:** The perpendicular design addresses the challenge of low-moisture conditions, a common limitation in microbial fuel cells. By positioning the anode horizontally and the cathode vertically, the top end of the fuel cell remains flush with the ground's surface. This design facilitates consistent airflow and prevents the accumulation of debris, ensuring sustained microbial activity even in dry soil.

3. **Hydration of the Cathode:** The vertical orientation of the cathode, with its lower end nestled deep beneath the surface, contributes to the fuel cell's adaptability to environmental changes. Even when surface soil dries out, the lower end

remains hydrated from the moist surrounding soil. This design feature addresses the challenge of maintaining hydration in low-moisture conditions.

4. **Gradual Drying After Floods:** In the event of floods, the fuel cell's vertical design allows for gradual drying of the cathode. This feature prevents abrupt drying, ensuring that the fuel cell remains operational after potential flood events. The fuel cell's adaptability to environmental changes, facilitated by the unique design, enhances its resilience and longevity.
5. **3D-Printed Cap for Protection:** The fuel cell incorporates a 3D-printed cap as a protective measure. This cap serves multiple purposes, including preventing debris from entering the fuel cell, maintaining air exchange, and shielding the internal components

from external elements. The 3D-printed cap is integral to the fuel cell's design, contributing to its durability and reliability.

6. **Consistent Airflow with Air Chamber:** The introduction of an empty air chamber running alongside the cathode is another unique feature. This air chamber ensures consistent airflow, supporting the necessary oxygen supply for microbial activity. The perpendicular design, combined with the air chamber, addresses challenges related to maintaining optimal conditions for microbial processes.

Incorporation of 3D-Printed Components

The use of 3D-printed components in the soil-microbe-powered fuel cell design showcases the integration of advanced manufacturing techniques to enhance functionality and protection.

1. **Cap for Debris Prevention:** The 3D-printed cap serves as a protective shield for the fuel cell. By covering the top of the device, it prevents debris from entering and potentially disrupting the internal components. This feature is crucial for maintaining the fuel cell's operational integrity in outdoor environments, ensuring reliable and uninterrupted energy generation.

2. **Airflow Management:** The cap plays a role in managing airflow within the fuel cell. It includes a hole on top and an empty air chamber alongside the cathode, contributing to consistent airflow. This design choice facilitates the necessary oxygen supply for microbial activity, addressing one

of the challenges faced by traditional microbial fuel cells in buried conditions.

3. **Customization and Rapid Prototyping:** The use of 3D printing allows for customization and rapid prototyping of components. This flexibility is advantageous during the design and testing phases, enabling the research team to iterate quickly and optimize the fuel cell's performance. The 3D-printed cap, specifically tailored to the fuel cell's dimensions, demonstrates the adaptability of this manufacturing method.

4. **Integration with Environmental Considerations:** 3D printing offers the advantage of using environmentally friendly materials, aligning with the sustainability goals of the soil-microbe-powered fuel cell.

The ability to choose materials with minimal environmental impact contributes to the overall eco-friendliness of the technology. Additionally, 3D printing allows for the efficient use of materials, reducing waste in the manufacturing process.

5. **Protection Against External Elements:** The 3D-printed cap, in conjunction with the fuel cell's overall design, protects against external elements. By covering the device, it shields the internal components from potential damage caused by weather conditions, dirt, or other environmental factors. This protective feature enhances the fuel cell's durability and ensures its functionality over an extended period.

6. **Accessibility and Affordability:** 3D printing technology enhances accessibility and affordability in

manufacturing. Components can be produced locally, reducing the need for complex supply chains and minimizing costs. This aligns with the researchers' goal of creating a technology that is not only sustainable in its operation but also in its production, making it accessible to a broader range of users and communities.

7. **Iterative Design Improvements:** The iterative nature of 3D printing enables continuous design improvements. As the research team tested different prototypes and gathered performance data, they could quickly implement changes to the 3D-printed components. This iterative design process is essential for refining the fuel cell's overall efficiency, adaptability, and resilience.

In conclusion, the incorporation of 3D-printed components in the design of the soil-microbe-powered fuel cell showcases the intersection of advanced engineering and manufacturing techniques. The 3D-printed cap, in particular, serves as a protective and functional element that contributes to the fuel cell's success in addressing challenges and realizing its potential as a sustainable and reliable energy technology.

Accessibility and Open Source Initiatives

Public Access to Designs, Tutorials, and Simulation Tools

The soil-microbe-powered fuel cell project led by Northwestern University distinguishes itself not only through its innovative technology but also through its commitment to accessibility and open-source initiatives. Providing public access to designs, tutorials, and simulation tools is a pivotal aspect of democratizing knowledge and fostering widespread adoption and development.

1. **Open Access to Designs:** One of the hallmark features of this initiative is the transparent sharing of designs. By making the blueprints and specifications of the soil-microbe-powered fuel cell freely accessible to the public, the research team encourages a broader audience to understand, replicate, and further innovate upon the technology. This open-access approach contributes to the democratization of sustainable energy solutions.

2. **Educational Tutorials:** In addition to design details, the project includes educational tutorials. These tutorials serve as valuable resources for students, researchers, and enthusiasts interested in understanding the principles behind the fuel cell's

operation. They provide step-by-step guides, enhancing the learning experience and empowering individuals to explore the realms of microbial fuel cell technology.

3. **Simulation Tools for Understanding:** Simulation tools play a crucial role in comprehending the intricacies of the fuel cell's behavior. By providing access to simulation tools, the project promotes a deeper understanding of how the technology interacts with different variables. This accessibility is particularly beneficial for researchers and engineers aiming to explore the potential applications and improvements in microbial fuel cell technology.

4. **Democratizing Knowledge:** The decision to open up designs, tutorials, and simulation tools reflects a

commitment to democratizing knowledge in the scientific and engineering communities. Breaking down barriers to access empowers individuals from diverse backgrounds to engage with the technology, fostering a culture of inclusivity and collaboration.

Encouraging Collaboration and Further Development

1. **Global Collaboration Opportunities:** Open-sourcing the soil-microbe-powered fuel cell project creates opportunities for global collaboration. Researchers, engineers, and innovators worldwide can contribute their expertise, insights, and improvements. This collaborative approach accelerates the development and refinement of the technology by leveraging the collective intelligence of a diverse community.

2. **Community Engagement:** The initiative encourages active participation from the broader community. Individuals with varying levels of expertise can engage in discussions, share experiences, and

propose enhancements. This inclusive approach not only enriches the development process but also fosters a sense of community ownership and shared responsibility for the success of the project.

3. **Iterative Improvement:** The open-source model facilitates an iterative improvement process. Contributors can suggest modifications, experiment with different materials or designs, and propose innovative solutions. This iterative approach is essential for the continuous enhancement of the fuel cell's efficiency, adaptability, and applicability across different contexts.

4. **Feedback Loop for Innovation:** Open source initiatives create a feedback loop for innovation. Users and contributors can provide real-world feedback based on their

experiences with the technology. This feedback becomes invaluable in identifying areas for improvement, addressing challenges, and uncovering potential applications that may not have been initially considered by the research team.

Advantages of Open Source Approach in Science and Engineering

1. **Accelerated Innovation:** The open-source approach accelerates innovation by tapping into the collective intelligence of a global community. Contributions from diverse perspectives lead to a rapid exchange of ideas and solutions, expediting the development and refinement of the technology. This

collaborative model contrasts with traditional closed systems, allowing for faster progress.

2. **Accessible to a Broad Audience:** Open source makes technology accessible to a broader audience. Researchers, students, hobbyists, and professionals can engage with the project, fostering a culture of inclusivity. This accessibility promotes learning, skill development, and participation in scientific and engineering advancements, irrespective of geographical or institutional constraints.

3. **Reducing Barriers to Entry:** Traditional research and development processes often involve high entry barriers, limiting access to resources and knowledge. Open source eliminates these barriers, enabling individuals or organizations with

limited resources to participate in the development and application of the technology. This democratization of innovation promotes a more equitable distribution of scientific advancements.

4. **Transparency and Accountability:** Open source promotes transparency in scientific and engineering endeavors. The visibility of design details, source code, and methodologies fosters accountability. The community can scrutinize, validate, and contribute to the project, ensuring a higher standard of quality and reliability. This transparency builds trust and confidence in the technology.

5. **Continuous Improvement:** An open-source model encourages continuous improvement. As users and contributors identify areas for

enhancement, the technology undergoes iterative refinement. This ongoing process of improvement ensures that the technology remains adaptable, resilient, and relevant to evolving needs and challenges.

6. **Community-Driven Solutions:** Open source empowers communities to find context-specific solutions. Local adaptations and innovations can emerge based on the unique requirements of different regions or industries. This community-driven approach enhances the versatility and applicability of the technology across diverse settings.

In conclusion, the accessibility and open-source initiatives associated with the soil-microbe-powered fuel cell project exemplify a transformative approach in science and engineering. By sharing knowledge, fostering collaboration, and embracing an inclusive model, the project not only advances the field of microbial fuel cells but also contributes to a global culture of innovation and sustainability.

Future Directions and Research Opportunities

Potential Improvements and Enhancements

The soil-microbe-powered fuel cell, developed by Northwestern University, has already demonstrated remarkable performance and sustainability. However, as with any innovative technology, there are opportunities for further improvements and enhancements to optimize its functionality and expand its potential applications.

1. **Increased Power Output:** Research can focus on techniques to further increase the power output of the fuel cell. This could involve optimizing microbial processes, enhancing the conductivity of materials, or exploring alternative configurations. Increasing power output would expand the range of devices that the fuel cell can effectively power.

2. **Enhanced Adaptability to Soil Conditions:** Improving the fuel cell's adaptability to a wider range of soil conditions is a crucial avenue for research. This could involve developing variations of the fuel cell that are specifically tailored to

different types of soil or environmental factors. A more versatile fuel cell would find applications in diverse agricultural and environmental settings.

3. **Long-Term Stability and Durability:** Research efforts can be directed towards achieving even greater long-term stability and durability. Investigating materials with extended lifespans, robust against environmental stressors, and resistant to degradation over time will contribute to the fuel cell's reliability, reducing maintenance requirements and extending its overall lifespan.
4. **Efficiency Optimization:** Further research can focus on optimizing the overall efficiency of the fuel cell. This includes investigating ways to reduce energy losses during microbial processes, enhancing the conversion of organic carbon into electricity, and

refining the design for improved electron flow. Higher efficiency translates to a more sustainable and economically viable energy solution.

5. **Integration with Energy Storage Systems:** Exploring ways to integrate the soil-microbe-powered fuel cell with energy storage systems can enhance its practicality. This could involve coupling the fuel cell with batteries or other storage technologies to store excess energy generated during optimal conditions. Energy storage integration ensures a more consistent power supply, particularly in fluctuating environmental conditions.

Exploration of Fully Biodegradable Materials

1. **Sustainable Material Selection:** A critical research direction involves exploring fully biodegradable materials for constructing the fuel cell components. This aligns with the broader goal of minimizing environmental impact. Investigating materials that can degrade harmlessly over time ensures that the fuel cell remains an eco-friendly technology from production to disposal.

2. **Biocompatibility with Soil Microbes:** The choice of materials should consider their biocompatibility with soil microbes. Research can delve into identifying materials that do not hinder microbial activity and maintain a harmonious interaction with the soil ecosystem. Biodegradable materials that naturally integrate into the soil environment contribute to the overall sustainability of the technology.

3. **Life Cycle Assessment:** Conducting a comprehensive life cycle assessment of the fuel cell, with a focus on biodegradable materials, is essential. This assessment should evaluate the environmental impact at each stage, from raw material extraction to manufacturing, use, and disposal. Understanding the complete life cycle informs decisions on material selection and provides insights into the technology's overall sustainability.

Integration with Emerging Technologies and IoT

1. **Internet of Things (IoT) Integration:** Research can explore the seamless integration of the soil-microbe-powered fuel cell with emerging technologies, particularly in the realm of the Internet of Things

(IoT). Enhancing the fuel cell's compatibility with IoT devices could enable real-time data monitoring, remote management, and advanced analytics. This integration opens avenues for precision agriculture and smart environmental monitoring.

2. **Sensor Diversity and Functionality:** Expanding the capabilities of the fuel cell to power a diverse array of sensors is an exciting research opportunity. This could involve developing sensors for additional environmental parameters, such as nutrient levels, pollution indicators, or microbial activity. Diversifying sensor functionality enhances the fuel cell's utility in various applications beyond soil moisture and touch detection.

3. **Autonomous Systems for Agriculture:** Investigating the

integration of the fuel cell into autonomous agricultural systems is a forward-looking research avenue. Autonomous robots or drones powered by soil-microbe fuel cells could revolutionize precision agriculture by providing continuous monitoring and targeted interventions based on real-time data. This aligns with the broader trend of leveraging renewable energy for sustainable and autonomous farming practices.

4. **Energy Harvesting Techniques:** Research can explore complementary energy harvesting techniques to supplement the soil-microbe-powered fuel cell. Integrating solar or wind energy harvesting with the microbial fuel cell could create hybrid systems that ensure a more consistent and reliable power supply. This approach maximizes energy capture from diverse environmental sources.

5. **Data Security and Privacy Considerations:** With the integration of IoT, research should address data security and privacy concerns. Implementing robust cybersecurity measures to protect data transmitted from the sensors to base stations is crucial. Ensuring the secure and private operation of the entire system is essential, especially in applications where sensitive agricultural or environmental data is involved.

In conclusion, the future directions and research opportunities for the soil-microbe-powered fuel cell are rich and diverse. By continually refining the technology, exploring sustainable materials, and integrating with emerging technologies, researchers can unlock new possibilities for this innovative energy solution, contributing to the advancement of sustainable and eco-friendly practices in agriculture and environmental monitoring.

Environmental and Social Impact

Reduction of Electronic Waste and Toxic Chemicals

1. **Mitigating E-Waste:** The soil-microbe-powered fuel cell offers a significant contribution to the reduction of electronic waste (e-waste). Unlike traditional batteries, which often contain toxic and non-biodegradable materials, the fuel cell operates sustainably with minimal environmental impact. By promoting a shift towards cleaner energy technologies, the fuel cell helps

mitigate the environmental consequences associated with the disposal of conventional electronic devices.

2. **Elimination of Hazardous Chemicals:** Traditional batteries, especially those with lithium and heavy metals, pose environmental hazards when improperly disposed of. The soil-microbe-powered fuel cell, powered by natural microbial processes, eliminates the need for toxic chemicals in its operation. This not only reduces the risk of soil and water contamination but also addresses concerns related to the extraction and processing of hazardous materials for battery production.

3. **Extended Lifespan and Durability:** The longevity and durability of the fuel cell contribute to its environmental impact. By lasting 120% longer than comparable technologies, the fuel cell minimizes the frequency of replacements, reducing the overall environmental

footprint associated with manufacturing, transportation, and disposal. This extended lifespan aligns with sustainable practices, promoting resource efficiency.

Contribution to Sustainable Development Goals

1. **Affordable and Clean Energy (SDG 7):** The soil-microbe-powered fuel cell aligns with Sustainable Development Goal 7 by providing an alternative, clean energy source. Its ability to harness energy from soil microbes offers a decentralized and sustainable solution, particularly for low-power applications. This contributes to the global effort to ensure access to affordable, reliable, sustainable, and modern energy for all.

2. **Sustainable Cities and Communities (SDG 11):** The technology holds potential implications for sustainable urban development. In precision agriculture, the fuel cell can power sensors that contribute to data-driven decision-making, promoting efficient land use and resource management. The reduction of electronic waste also aligns with the creation of sustainable and resilient cities.

3. **Responsible Consumption and Production (SDG 12):** Addressing concerns related to electronic waste, the fuel cell exemplifies responsible consumption and production practices. Utilizing biodegradable materials and extending the lifespan of the technology, supports the transition to sustainable production and consumption patterns,

minimizing negative environmental impacts.

4. **Climate Action (SDG 13):** The fuel cell's reliance on natural microbial processes and avoidance of traditional battery materials contribute to climate action. By reducing the demand for resource-intensive and environmentally harmful components, the technology aligns with efforts to combat climate change. Additionally, the energy harvesting process has lower associated carbon emissions compared to conventional energy sources.

Implications for Global Energy and Environmental Policy

1. **Renewable Energy Integration:** The soil-microbe-powered fuel cell aligns with global energy policies focused on transitioning to renewable and sustainable energy sources. Its innovative approach to energy generation provides policymakers with a model for integrating microbial fuel cells into broader renewable energy strategies. This could influence policy decisions favoring the adoption of eco-friendly technologies.

2. **Circular Economy Initiatives:** The fuel cell contributes to the principles of a circular economy by minimizing waste and promoting resource efficiency. Its use of fully biodegradable materials aligns with

policies aimed at reducing the environmental impact of electronic devices. Policymakers may consider supporting and incentivizing similar circular economy initiatives that prioritize sustainable materials and design.

3. **Technology Access and Affordability:** The open-source nature of the fuel cell project has implications for global technology access. Policymakers may recognize the value of initiatives that make sustainable technologies accessible and affordable. Supporting open-source projects can become a policy strategy to ensure that advancements in science and engineering benefit diverse communities and contribute to global sustainability goals.

4. **Regulatory Frameworks for Sustainable Technologies:** The emergence of innovative technologies like the soil-microbe-powered fuel cell prompts policymakers to develop regulatory frameworks that support sustainable alternatives. This includes establishing standards for eco-friendly materials, incentivizing research and development in green technologies, and implementing measures to reduce the environmental impact of electronic devices.

5. **International Collaboration on Sustainable Solutions:** The global impact of electronic waste necessitates international collaboration on sustainable solutions. The soil-microbe-powered fuel cell, with its potential to reduce e-waste, becomes a case study for international cooperation. Policymakers may explore partnerships and agreements

to promote the adoption of sustainable technologies and share best practices for environmental conservation.

In conclusion, the environmental and social impact of the soil-microbe-powered fuel cell extends beyond technological innovation. Its implications for reducing electronic waste, contributing to sustainable development goals, and influencing global energy and environmental policies underscore the transformative potential of eco-friendly technologies in addressing pressing global challenges. Policymakers play a crucial role in supporting and shaping a future where such innovations lead the way toward a more sustainable and resilient world.

Conclusion

The development of soil-microbe-powered fuel cells represents a significant milestone in sustainable energy technology. Through innovative engineering, open-source collaboration, and a commitment to environmental responsibility, this groundbreaking technology offers promising solutions to pressing challenges in energy generation and environmental conservation.

Summary of Key Findings and Contributions

The soil-microbe-powered fuel cell harnesses the natural processes of soil microbes to generate electricity, providing a renewable and eco-friendly alternative to traditional battery systems. Key findings from the research include:

- We have demonstrated performance in diverse soil conditions, outperforming traditional technologies by 120%.
- Integration of 3D-printed components for durability, debris prevention, and efficient airflow management.

- Open-source accessibility enables widespread adoption, collaboration, and innovation.

Significance of Soil-Microbe-Powered Fuel Cells in Sustainable Energy Landscape

The emergence of soil-microbe-powered fuel cells holds profound implications for the sustainable energy landscape:

- **Environmental Sustainability**: By reducing electronic waste and minimizing reliance on toxic chemicals, these fuel cells promote environmentally responsible energy generation.

- **Resource Efficiency:** Utilizing biodegradable materials and promoting long-term durability contribute to a circular economy model, emphasizing resource efficiency and waste reduction.

- **Community Empowerment:** Open-source initiatives empower communities to engage in sustainable technology development, fostering inclusivity and knowledge sharing.

- **Global Impact:** The scalability and adaptability of soil-microbe-powered fuel cells make them viable solutions for diverse applications worldwide, from precision agriculture to environmental monitoring.

Call to Action for Further Research and Implementation

As we look to the future, there are several critical areas for further research and implementation:

- **Enhanced Performance:** Continued research is needed to optimize the performance and efficiency of soil-microbe-powered fuel cells, ensuring reliability and scalability across various environments.

- **Technological Integration:** Exploring opportunities for integrating fuel cell technology with emerging IoT devices and renewable energy systems can unlock new applications and enhance sustainability efforts.

- **Policy Support:** Policymakers play a pivotal role in supporting the development and adoption of sustainable technologies. Implementing regulatory frameworks, incentives, and funding mechanisms can accelerate the transition towards eco-friendly energy solutions.

- **Global Collaboration:** International collaboration and knowledge sharing are essential for advancing sustainable energy initiatives. Building partnerships and networks can facilitate the exchange of best practices, research findings, and resources to address shared environmental challenges.

In conclusion, soil-microbe-powered fuel cells represent a beacon of hope in the quest for sustainable energy solutions. Through interdisciplinary collaboration, innovation, and a collective commitment to environmental stewardship, we can harness the power of nature to create a cleaner, greener, and more resilient future for generations to come. Let us embrace the challenge and opportunity to shape a world powered by sustainability and ingenuity.

Milton Keynes UK
Ingram Content Group UK Ltd.
UKHW020335031224
451863UK00012B/555